Other Books by Harriet E. Huntington

CALIFORNIA HARBORS

CARGOES

FOREST GIANTS
   The Story of the California Redwoods

LET'S GO OUTDOORS

LET'S GO TO THE BROOK

LET'S GO TO THE DESERT

LET'S GO TO THE SEASHORE

PRAYING MANTIS

TUNE UP
   Instruments of the Orchestra

THE YOSEMITE STORY

THE YOSEMITE STORY

written and illustrated with photographs
by HARRIET E. HUNTINGTON
drawings by J. Noël

DOUBLEDAY & COMPANY, INC.   GARDEN CITY, NEW YORK

This book is dedicated to John Muir and François E. Matthes

Contents

1 Discovery and Development of Yosemite 9

2 The Ancestral Mountain Systems and
   Uplifts of the Sierra Nevada 19

3 Glaciation 33

4 The Sierra Escarpment 55

5 Granite Types and Master Joints 59

6 Domes and Exfoliation 73

7 Erosion in the Sierra 77

   Appendix 86

   Map of Yosemite National Park, California 90

   Glossary 91

   Suggested Reading 93

   Geological Timetable 94

   Index 96

CHAPTER 1

Discovery and Development of Yosemite

Not many places on this earth have such an awe-inspiring display of sculptured mountains as the Yosemite Valley. The magnificent waterfalls, the constant-flowing Merced River, the enormous granite cliffs, and the mammoth rocks carved and shaped by nature make the Yosemite a valley without equal. To understand how the valley was formed, and to realize that the process of creation took a vast length of time, both add meaning to its beauty.

Yosemite Valley lies 150 miles east of San Francisco and is in the center of the Sierra Nevada. The Sierra Nevada is the longest, highest unbroken mountain range in California or, for that matter, in the United States. It lies about 120 miles inland in the central part of California and trends northwest and southeast for about 430 miles parallel to the Pacific Coast. Its foothills slope gradually upward from the Sacramento and San Joaquin valleys eastward for about forty to eighty miles to the 11,000-foot average height of the crest. From the main crest there is a sharp decline of a few miles to the eastern edge of the range. Loosely translated from the Spanish, Sierra Nevada means "snowy mountain range." Most of the eastern side of the Sierra Nevada lies within the California border, but a bit of it around Lake Tahoe extends into Nevada.

The Yosemite Valley remained undiscovered by the white man until 1833, when it was seen from a distance by a mountaineer, Joseph Reddeford Walker. Guided by Indians he crossed the Sierra Nevada from the east through Mono Pass, went west over the uplands but probably to the north of the Yosemite Valley, and down the foothills to the San Joaquin Valley.

On October 18, 1849, William Penn Abrams wrote in his diary of his accidental visit to the valley, but the credit of the discovery is usually given to Major James D. Savage. In March of 1851 a group of men led by Major Savage went on a punitive mission after the marauding U-zu-ma-ti Indian tribe. Pursuing the U-zu-ma-ti chief, Ten-ei-ya, the volunteers stumbled upon the tribe's home in the valley.

Yosemite Valley from the eastern portal of Wawona tunnel, looking eastward. El Capitan is on the left; Clouds Rest, Half Dome, and Sentinel Rock are in the center; while Bridalveil Fall and its hanging valley are on the right.

Following the old Indian trail over the uplands south of Merced River, the battalion first saw the valley from Old Inspiration Point. The view from Old Inspiration Point is approximately the same view as that from the present parking area at the eastern portal of Wawona tunnel on the Wawona Road (State Highway 41) from Fresno, California.

From Old Inspiration Point looking eastward up and across the valley, past the Rockslides, they could see the rock of El Capitan on the north wall. Opposite on the southern wall was Bridalveil Fall and its hanging valley. Looking farther up the valley to the east end, the volunteers could see the tops of Half Dome and Clouds Rest over Sentinel Rock.

Looking southward, Cathedral Rocks are opposite El Capitan. The tops of the rocks rise 1650, 2590, and 2680 feet above the Yosemite Valley floor. The backs of these rocks form the western side of the Bridalveil Valley. You can see in the opposite picture the sloping western side of Bridalveil Valley.

Not until the men descended into the valley and made their camp at the foot of El Capitan could they begin to realize how massive the rocks were. One member of the party, LaFayette H. Bunnel, kept a diary of the expedition and tells in his account of the finding of the valley: "One official estimated El Capitan at 400 feet, Captain Boling at 800 feet. . . . My estimate was a sheer perpendicularity of at least 1,500 feet."

But all were wrong. Actually the cliff measures 3000 from toe to brow. Its crown is 500 feet higher.

When the volunteers returned to Mariposa, the news of the valley's existence was made public. Members of the battalion named the Yosemite Valley after the U-zu-ma-ti Indian tribe. U-zu-ma-ti means "grizzly bear." But the Indians themselves called the valley Ah-wah-nee, which means "deep, grassy valley."

The Indians were not immediately subdued, and for a couple of years there was continued fighting. Some of the Indians were killed; others were taken prisoner and put on an Indian reservation, where they sickened and died. A few escaped to live with the neighboring tribe at Mono Lake. Today, as far as is known, there is not a full-blooded Yosemite Indian alive.

In 1855 James M. Hutchings led the first party of tourists. On this trip Thomas A. Ayres, an artist, sketched the valley. These

This view from Glacier Point Road, looking westward, shows the terrain of the western slope of the Sierra Nevada below Yosemite Gorge. The Merced River is below and the Coast Range is in the background. Glacier Point Road follows an old Indian trail for some distance.

sketches and Hutchings' articles helped to spread the fame of the valley.

The valley was difficult to reach. At first people went in by horseback, taking a couple of days to make the journey over the uplands from Mariposa. Then in 1874 two wagon roads were built into the valley from Merced on the northern side of Merced River. In 1875 another wagon road from Mariposa was opened which entered the valley on the southern side of the Merced River. At that time four-horse stages carrying tourists made the trip, which was uncomfortable to say the least. The dirt road, steep and rough, was dusty in summer and muddy in spring.

In 1907 the Yosemite Valley Railroad was opened. It ran alongside the Merced River as far as the little settlement of El Portal. From there tourists traveled fifteen miles up to the valley by horse stage. But in 1937 several miles of track along the river bed were washed out and the railroad was abandoned. With the advent of automobiles, motor stages entered the valley in 1913. Today there are several highways which enter Yosemite National Park.

So striking is Yosemite Valley that its beauty was recognized early in an age when little or no thought was given to the preservation of America's wilderness. Public-minded Californians convinced U. S. Senator John Conness that it should be preserved for the enjoyment of future generations. In 1864 President Lincoln signed an act of Congress which gave the State of California Yosemite Valley and Mariposa Big Tree Grove to administer.

Before Glacier Point Road was built, tourists on horseback traveled through the upland forests, following narrow trails and fording creeks, which looked the same as Bridalveil Creek does today.

Looking northward from Glacier Point. The top of Upper Yosemite Fall rises a little more than 2500 feet above the valley floor; the fall itself is about 1500 feet. The lower fall is 320 feet high, about twice the height of Niagara Falls.

But it remained for John Muir, a Scottish-born naturalist, to make the public aware of the need for conservation. Through many articles in well-known western and eastern magazines and newspapers from 1871 to 1890 he made his readers National Park conscious. He was appalled by the destruction caused by sheep grazing, timber logging and public misuse, and his pleas to save the Sierra and Yosemite region awakened the nation to the value of unspoiled wilderness.

Looking northeast from Glacier Point. Basket Dome is above North Dome, which is in turn above the Royal Arches. To the left of the Royal Arches is another set of arches. Washington Column is to the right of the Royal Arches.

In 1890 Sequoia and General Grant National Parks were founded. In the same year, Yosemite National Park was established around the Yosemite Grant. Later in 1905 the State of California redeeded Yosemite Valley and Mariposa Big Tree Grove to the Federal Government and they were included in Yosemite National Park. In 1916 a Congressional bill for the establishment of the present National Park Service was signed by President Woodrow Wilson.

Sequoias in Mariposa Big Tree Grove in Yosemite National Park, reprinted from Forest Giants, *by the author.*

To help maintain continued interest in the Sierra Nevada, John Muir founded the Sierra Club in 1892. The club's purpose is to "explore, enjoy, and render accessible the mountain region of the Pacific Coast; to publish authentic information concerning them; to enlist the support and cooperation of the people and government in preserving the forests and other natural features of the Sierra Nevada."

Although Muir first went to Yosemite in 1868, it was not until a return trip the following year that he saw what he felt was evidence of glaciers having traveled through the valleys and uplands. Muir had studied the findings of the then famous European authority on glaciers, Louis Agassiz, and disagreed with the opinion of Josiah Whitney, the official geologist of California. Whitney, in answer to questions from tourists as to how the valley had been formed, replied, "By a primal cataclysm, a great catastrophy . . . The bottom of the valley sank down to an unknown depth owing to its support being withdrawn from underneath." Whitney in his "Official Guide Book to Yosemite Valley" stated, "There is no reason to suppose . . . that glaciers have ever occupied the valley, or any portion of it."

By 1870, Muir seriously began to gather facts to support his theory—that the main sculpturing of the valley had been done by glaciers. In the following years he tramped over the valleys and uplands and found evidence of glacial erosion, even active glaciers. He had evidence that his theory was correct.

François E. Matthes, topographer and geologist for the United States Geological Survey, in his extensive study of Yosemite Valley and the Sierra Nevada, corroborated Muir's belief of glacial erosion of the valley. Today it is agreed that the valley was sculptured by water and ice.

Geologists are constantly finding new facts which support and refine "proven" theories or new facts which disprove the "proven" theories. Geologists do not always agree with each other—one interprets a fact one way, while another geologist interprets the same fact another way. Who knows, perhaps someday Whitney's belief that a catastrophe created Yosemite Valley may be corroborated. Geologists do not know beyond a doubt what forces caused the earth's crust to be as it is and cannot state that a theory is absolutely true.

During the summers of 1905 and 1906 Matthes, as official topographer for the United States Geological Survey, mapped Yosemite Valley. On the back of the map is printed an essay which Matthes wrote on the valley's geological history. François E. Matthes wrote more than fifteen geological essays about the valley and the Sierra Nevada which the Sierra Club published. Matthes' first geological assignment was to study the origin of Yosemite Valley and to write his findings in layman's language. In 1930 he completed his report, which included a history of the Sierra Nevada. Matthes used a camera to illustrate some of the special geological features. (The monumental work was entitled "Geological History of the Yosemite Valley, Geological Professional Paper 160." It was published by the United States Geological Survey.)

Of all the men who loved Yosemite Valley the names of John Muir, François E. Matthes, and Ansel Adams are the most prominent. We owe a debt to John Muir not only for expressing his love

Part of Yosemite Valley's southern wall west of Sentinel Rock.

of nature in his writings but also for his fight for the preservation of the valley's beauty; to François E. Matthes for his geological explanation of its grandeur; and to Ansel Adams for capturing the valley's moods and the essence of its beauty in his photographs. It is fitting that some of Muir's and Matthes' writings have been published and illustrated with Ansel Adams' pictures.

CHAPTER 2

The Ancestral Mountain Systems and Uplifts of the Sierra Nevada

Earth, our planet, is about five billion years old. Although the exact details of its long history will never be known, many scientists agree that the earth had its beginning as a mass of gases. The gases were attracted to each other and because of gravitational attraction came closer and closer together. They were condensed and eventually became liquid rock and water vapor. The heavier materials in the liquid rock slowly moved toward the core.

As the earth cooled, the lighter materials formed an outer crust of rock, which slowly solidified to form the continents. While the cooling process continued, water vapor condensed from the gaseous envelope and created oceans by rains that may have lasted for billions of years. During this time great stresses within the earth ruptured the rock, causing earthquakes which jarred the earth's surface. Internal pressures raised the crustal rocks to form mountains. Molten rock materials spewed forth by volcanic eruptions and, welling up from deep within the crust, created other mountains.

Then began the constant and inescapable processes of weathering and erosion. Innumerable rainstorms gradually carved river valleys. Rains washed rocks and rock particles down mountains, into valleys and rivers. Rocks broke up as they tumbled down mountains and were rolled against other rocks in rivers. Eventually the rocks of the mountains were ground into pebbles, sand, and mud. Rivers transported these sediments and deposited them in valleys, over flatlands, and into oceans, where they settled on the bottom. It is almost impossible to comprehend the length of time it took the forces of nature to cause these geological happenings. These forces work so slowly that the changes which are going on today are almost imperceptible.

Because Yosemite Valley is part of the Sierra Nevada, the histories of the two are linked together. Therefore, to understand Yosemite Valley's past one must also learn the story of the Sierra Nevada.

About 600 million years ago the area which is now the Sierra Nevada was covered by a shallow sea. This sea extended over the eastern half of California, into Nevada and Utah. In its waters tiny sea animals lived and died. Their shells made calcium deposits or sediments. These sediments along with sand, mud, silt, salts, and minerals washed into the sea from the surrounding land, and formed layers—called strata. Gradually over a long time the layers of sediments were hardened into strata of sedimentary rocks either by pressure from the strata above or by being cemented with chemical and minerals. Mud, sand, and calcium became shale, sandstone, and limestone respectively.

By the end of this period, which lasted at least 350 million years, the sediments were thousands of feet thick. As these sediments were deposited, part of the earth's crust beneath them was depressed. Later the strata were uplifted, folded, and crumpled into mountain

Pacific Ocean Coast Range Great California Valley Sierra Nevada

This profile drawing of the Yosemite National Park area in the Sierra Nevada shows sediments collected in the inland shallow sea. Geologists do not know how far into the present Pacific Ocean the land extended. The height of the land is exaggerated.

This drawing shows the same area as above, after the sediments in the shallow sea were pushed upward to form the first ancestral mountain system. An arm of the Pacific Ocean had appeared over the eastern part of California. The height of the land masses is exaggerated.

Pacific Ocean Coast Range Great California Valley Sierra Nevada

ranges. These mountains, which covered the area now occupied by the Sierra Nevada, are called the first ancestral mountain system.

Before and during the time the sedimentary rocks were being pushed upward into mountains, they were metamorphosed or changed by heat and pressure within the earth's crust into metamorphic rocks. Shale, limestone, and sandstone became respectively slate, marble, and quartzite.

Strata of the Calaveras Formation in the Merced River off Highway 140, eleven miles west of Yosemite National Park.

On the western side of the Sierra Nevada, particularly in the Merced Canyon below Yosemite National Park, there are remains of the metamorphic rocks of the first ancestral mountain system. These rocks are called the Calaveras Formation. Geologists call any unit of rock which is distinct from the surrounding rock a formation. Formations extend from one mile to hundreds of miles.

The best examples of the Calaveras Formation can be seen in and along the sides of the Merced River on Highway 140 approximately eleven miles west of Arch Rock Ranger Station. On the cliff side of the road the strata of highly metamorphosed slate is lustrous black. But it also is colored rusty red along the small cracks where the iron it contains has oxidized. The wrinkled, crumpled strata in the Merced River are various shades of gray. The iron has been leached or washed out by the river water. These rocks of the Calaveras Formation are the oldest in Yosemite National Park.

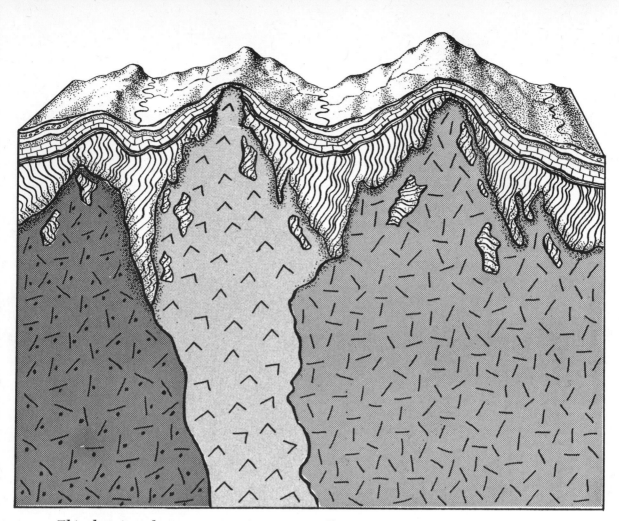

This drawing shows masses of magma welling upward and intruding into the metamorphic and sedimentary rocks of the first and second ancestral mountain systems.

About 150 million years ago the first ancestral mountain system was partly eroded away. The material deposited from the erosion depressed the land, and the land slowly sank once more to become the bottom of another shallow sea. More sediments collected and covered the remains of the first ancestral mountain system.

About 130 million years ago the new sediments with the underlying sediments of the first ancestral mountain system rose, folded, and crumpled to become a second ancestral mountain system. At the same time masses of magma or molten rock beneath the earth's crust were forced upward and into the new mountain folds. Over a period of twenty million years or more this hot magma slowly welled upward and, while still beneath the second mountain system, it cooled and crystalized into granite. It is this granite which forms the present-day Sierra Nevada.

The upper magma cooled and cracked, and the cracks were

filled with molten material from the center parts which had remained hot and fluid. Some of the fractures were filled quickly by thin fluid magma. This also crystalized into a kind of granite, called aplite, and, like mortar between two bricks, cemented the fractured granite together. The sealed cracks, called dikes, are found throughout the Sierra Nevada. They are from half an inch to several feet or more thick and up to hundreds of feet long.

Over a period of about fifty million years, weathering and erosion processes reduced the second ancestral mountain system to rows of hills. In some places the metamorphic rocks were worn away and the granite was exposed.

Unlike the two ancestral mountain systems, the present Sierra Nevada was not formed by folding strata, because the underlying granite was too thick and rigid to bend. Instead, the granite fractured along its edges and gradually was thrust upward in one gigantic block. The Sierra granite block is over 430 miles long

Dikes of aplite along Big Oak Flat Road above Yosemite Gorge. The cream-colored aplite is very hard and has a fine-grained texture.

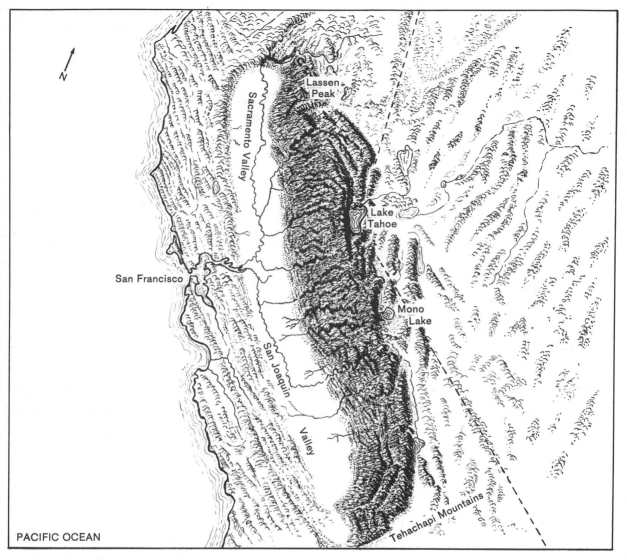

On this topographic map of the present-day Sierra Nevada the dotted lines show the approximate boundaries of the block. The western edge is buried under as much as 15,000 feet of soil, sand, and gravel deposits.

and between forty to eighty miles wide. The extent of its thickness is unknown, but geologists believe it to be tens of thousands of feet. The Sierra block is like an iceberg in that its greater part is below the earth's surface.

Then about sixty million years ago the block covered by the hills of the second ancestral mountain system and the remains of the first ancestral mountain system was upwarped and tilted. The eastern

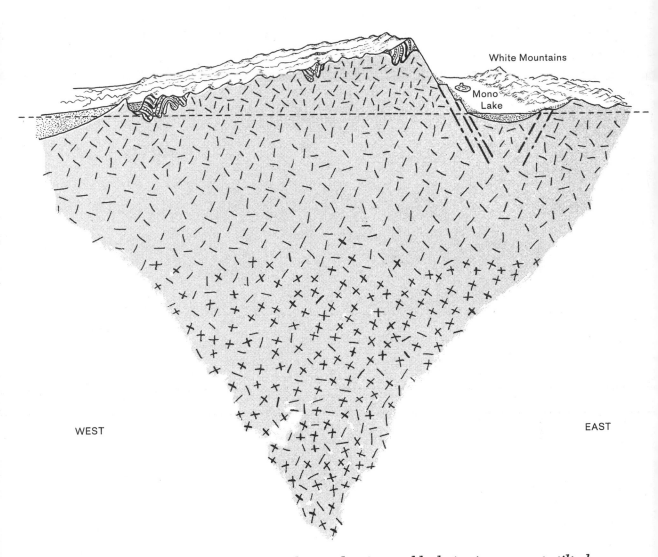

WEST

EAST

White Mountains

Mono Lake

This profile drawing shows the Sierra block in its present tilted position, and its "roots" of granite going down thousands of feet into the earth. The height of the mountain is greatly exaggerated.

side was pushed upward about 100 feet. The western edge did not sink but remained approximately in the same position. This created an unsymmetrical mountain range. The long, gradual western slope to the crest extended over four fifths of the range's width, while the eastern side declined rapidly. Although the country to the east also rose with the Sierra block, it did not rise as high. The land extending for about 400 miles eastward was broken into smaller fault-block ranges.

Up until this time the rivers flowed generally northwest or southeast, because the ancestral mountain systems were folded in parallel ranges running northwest. As the granite block tilted toward the southwest most of the rivers changed their courses to run down the western slope. Smaller rivers retained their northern or southern courses and became tributary streams.

The rivers and their tributary streams continued wearing away the metamorphic rocks of the second and first ancestral mountain systems until the mountains were not much higher than 100 to 1000 feet. At the same time, more of the underlying granite was exposed and became the tops of the highest hills.

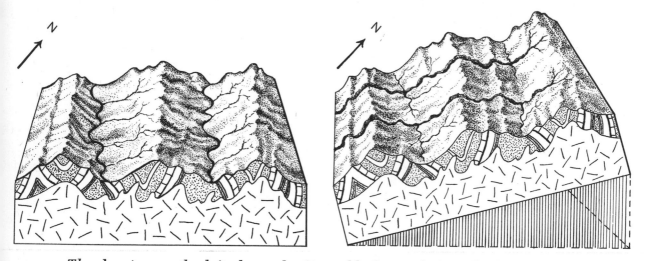

The drawing on the left shows the Sierra block area before the uplift, when the rivers ran north and south. The drawing on the right shows the Sierra block after the tilting when the rivers changed their courses to run westward.

One might say that Yosemite Valley was born when the ancient Merced River began to flow westward, because then the river started to sculpture the valley. At first the river meandered through a broad valley and had a shallow bed. As time passed, the Merced River slowly but surely cut deeper.

After the first major uplift the Sierra block was raised still more in a series of minor rises. For millions of years the block moved upward both slowly, a fraction of an inch at a time, and rapidly, during earthquakes, from several inches to a few feet at a time. These uplifts continued until about twelve million years ago when there was a second major uplift. At that time the rate of uplifts increased and the mountain crests rose several thousand feet.

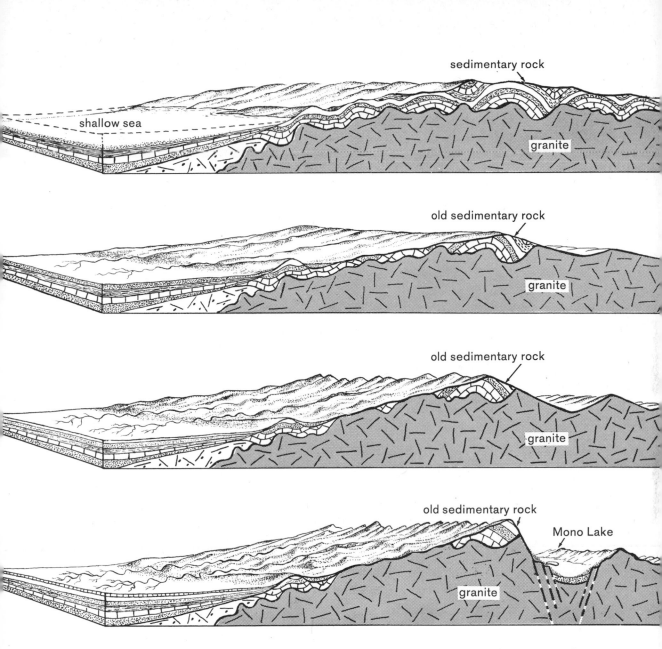

The above drawings show the positions of the Sierra block from the first uplift to the present day. A shows the Sierra Nevada after the granite intruded the metamorphic and sedimentary rocks of the first and second ancestral mountain systems; B, C, and D are the same section of the Sierra Nevada in the vicinity of Yosemite National Park. In B, after the first uplift, most of the sedimentary and metamorphic rock has been eroded and the rock debris has washed down into San Joaquin Valley. In C, after the second uplift, much more of the metamorphic rock is worn away and added to the existing sediments in San Joaquin Valley. D shows the changes after the third uplift and the downfaulting of the land to the east in the vicinity of Mono Lake. All land heights are exaggerated.

At the end of the second uplift, the ancient Yosemite Chasm was probably similar to this present-day canyon in the Merced River about a mile below the South Fork of the Merced River, as seen from Highway 140, looking westward.

Because the eastern side of the granite block was tilted higher in the second uplift, the western slope became steeper, causing the Merced River to flow faster, giving it more cutting power. The river cut a straighter course and created a V-shaped canyon 800 feet deep.

The third period of rapid uplifts began about a million or more years ago. During this time the mountains rose approximately to

At the end of the third uplift, the ancient Yosemite Chasm was 3000 feet deep and similar in appearance to this view of the Merced Gorge, looking southeast from Big Oak Flat Road.

their present height. This uplift increased the speed of the already swift Merced River, which then carved the V-shaped Yosemite Canyon into a narrow chasm 300 feet deep.

When the Sierra Nevada crest rose to an average height of 12,000 feet, it created a barrier to the rain clouds brought inland by the prevailing westerly winds. The barrier made the clouds rise up into the colder altitudes and caused the clouds to drop their

The sides of the ancient Yosemite Chasm looked somewhat like this view of the northern wall of Yosemite Valley to the east of Yosemite Falls.

moisture on the western slopes of the mountains. This heavy rainfall weathered the exposed rocks, and erosion left the sides of the ancient Yosemite Valley jagged and craggy.

The Merced River was joined at right angles by tributary streams which flowed over fairly level uplands. The tributaries were not powerful or big enough to dig their beds as deep as the chasm of the Merced River. When the streams reached the edge of the

Today, Cascade Fall tumbles furiously down the northern side of Yosemite Gorge much as it did after the third major uplift.

Merced Chasm, they cascaded furiously down its steep and rugged sides, leaving their own side valleys suspended or hanging. Thus, the name hanging valley is given to a tributary valley whose floor is higher than that of the main valley floor. As the Merced River dug its bed deeper, the tributary valleys were left hanging even higher.

In these side valleys and over the uplands, Giant Sequoias and other conifers began to grow in the high altitudes, where it was cooler. Slowly the climate changed, becoming colder, and rain started to descend as snow. The ice age was about to begin.

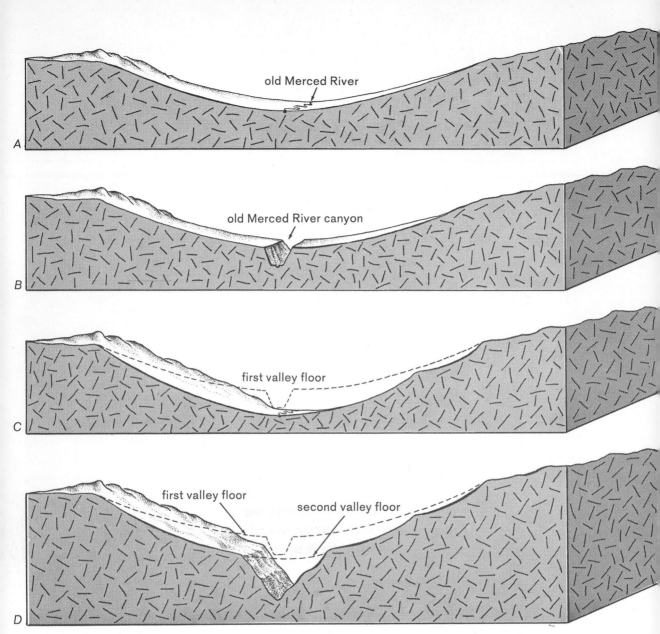

The above drawings illustrate how the Merced River excavated *Yosemite Canyon. A shows the broad valley after the first Sierra uplift when the Merced River began to flow westward. B shows the canyon after the second uplift when the young river cut a V-shaped nick in the broad valley. C shows the valley long after the second uplift, when the V-shaped nick had had time to broaden and become gentle sloping sides. The uplands were left as hanging valleys. The dotted lines indicate the profile of the former valley. D shows the canyon or valley within a valley after the third uplift. The uplands and the old valley's sides were left as two groups of hanging valleys. The dotted lines indicate the profile of the two former valleys.*

CHAPTER 3

Glaciation

The great ice age, which sculptured Yosemite Valley to approximately what it is today, began a million or more years ago. During this time there were several separate stages, each of which probably lasted about 10,000 to 100,000 years. There were even longer periods in between when the ice melted and disappeared. Then grasses, bushes, and trees grew again. During these warmer periods rain and rivers resumed their processes of weathering and erosion.

Unlike the northern part of North America, which was covered completely by a sheet of ice, the Sierra Nevada was spotted with valley glaciers and ice fields. In the high parts of the Sierra Nevada, glaciers originated in protected places where the westerly winds could not blow away loose snow and where shade kept the snow from melting. In the glacial stages more snow fell each winter than could melt during the summer. It accumulated, compacted, and turned into ice. When this ice reached the thickness of about 250 feet, its own weight made it spread, and gravity caused it to move downhill as a glacier.

Glaciers travel from a fraction of an inch to tens of feet each year. An active glacier maintains its length since new ice forms faster than the glacier can melt or evaporate. Depending upon the snowfall and air temperature, glaciers enlarge and advance, or remain stationary, or melt and recede.

In the first and second glacial stages, ice filled the Yosemite Chasm to the rim and covered the surrounding uplands. Only the tops of the tallest peaks, such as Half Dome, El Capitan, and Clouds Rest, rose like islands above a sea of ice. The glaciers reached a mile or more west of the present site of the village of El Portal before they melted. During the last glacial stage the ice did not cover as much territory. At that time the ancient Yosemite glacier, which was formed by the joining of two other extinct glaciers, Tenaya and Merced, filled one third of the valley's depth and reached a little below Bridalveil Fall.

When a glacier flowed down it plucked out, picked up, and

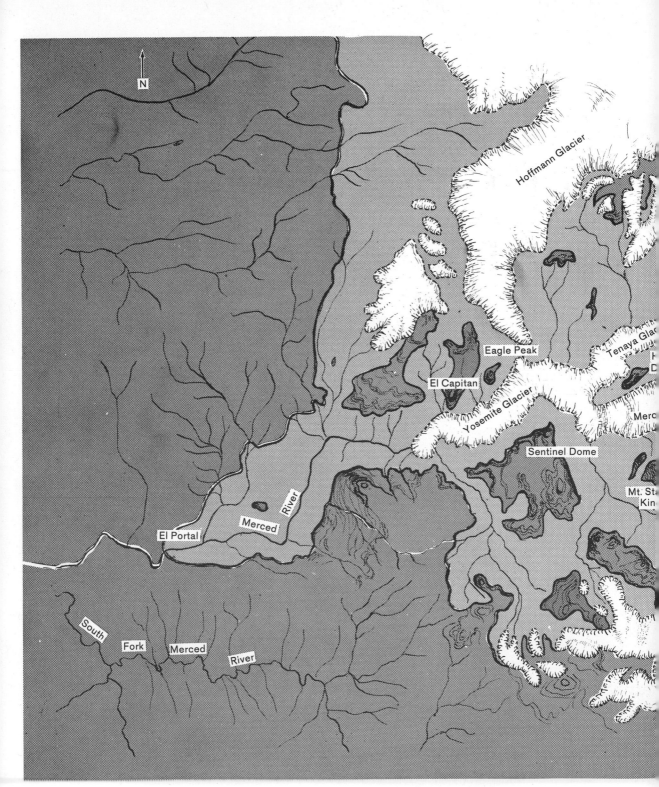

Map of the Yosemite National Park area showing the glaciated areas in light gray shading; the areas unglaciated during the early glacial periods in white; and the ice of the last glacial age in dark gray shading.

Cathedral Peak

Cathedral Range

Cathedral Range

Tuolumne Ice Field

Kuna Crest

ouds Rest

acier

Mt. Maclure

Marie Lake

Mt. Lyell

Merced Ice Field

River

Illilouette Glacier

Joaquin

San

sta Glacier

Looking south toward Kuna Crest across Dana Meadows, which are above Tuolumne Meadows. This alpine scene of melting winter snow gives an idea of what the glaciers and ice fields looked like when they were thawing between glacial periods.

carried away rocks of all sizes by freezing them into its bottom and sides. As the ancient glaciers formed they eroded recesses into the mountains. Underneath the head of a glacier and around its top, the rocks which were loosened by the expanding force of freezing water in their cracks tumbled down onto the glacier and were carried away. Gradually the areas at the head of the glacier were enlarged and deepened into steep-walled, semicircular hollows, called cirques.

The carved-out area is a cirque formed by glacial action. This cirque is above Lake Ellery on Highway 120 just outside Yosemite National Park. The patches of snow are not glaciers and will melt by midsummer.

While the glaciers flowed down the valleys, rocks which fell from the sides of the valley tumbled to the edge of the ice, where they were caught by the glacier. Most of the rocks that dropped onto the top of the glacier settled to its bottom. Some rocks that fell onto the glacier near its foot remained on top.

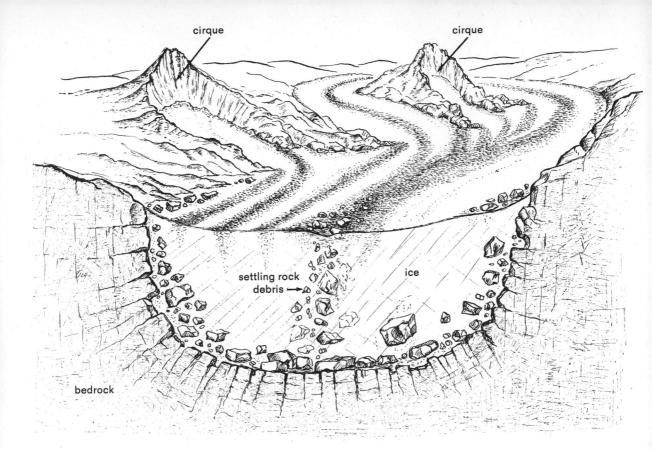

Cross section of a glacier showing its load of rocks and how it plucks them from the sides of the valley-canyon. The rocks in the middle were plucked from the sides of tributary canyons before their individual glaciers flowed into the main or trunk glacier.

A glacier excavated the canyon sides by plucking out the exposed or outside rock. Then the next or inside rock became exposed and was in position to be pried out. The boulders and rocks acted like shovels prying and digging out others. The glacier also was like a bulldozer which pushed rock debris, loose soil, and even trees to the sides and in front of it.

At the end of the glacier the ice melted and released its load

This drawing shows the zones of heavy snow accumulation and of ice wastage by melting or evaporation.

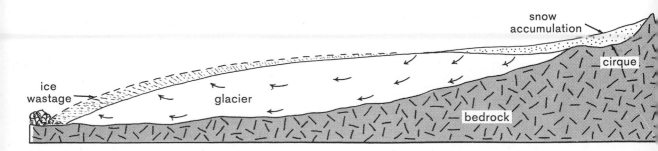

lateral moraines

glacier

terminal or recessional moraines

This drawing shows a receding glacier and two recessional moraines. The moraines are the ridges of boulders, rocks, and soil left by the glacier. The melting water from the glacier has eroded two openings in the moraines. The ice at the end of the glaciers is not so high as in the main body of a glacier.

of boulders, pebbles, sand, and clay. Unlike river sediment, in which the heaviest rocks gravitate to the bottom, glacial debris has rocks of various sizes mixed together. When the end of a glacier remains in one place long enough, the rock debris is deposited in a ridge, called a moraine. Because the end of a glacier is rounded, the debris forms a curved moraine. When a glacier recedes at an uneven rate, it leaves a series of moraines which are from

This drawing shows the outwash, end moraine, ground moraine, and eroded bedrock.

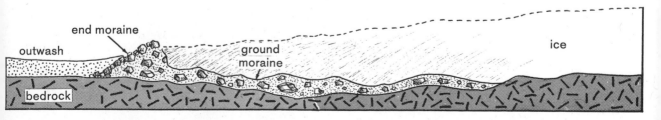

outwash

end moraine

ground moraine

ice

bedrock

ten to sixty feet in height. There are many moraines all over the Sierra Nevada. It is by finding and following them that geologists can tell where glaciers have been.

When boulders and rocks were transported on top of a glacier, they remained angular. Those that were dragged on the bottom of the glacier and ground against the bedrock have flat surfaces. A boulder that has been transported by ice is called an erratic boulder. Usually it is of a different type of rock from that upon which it rests. There are many erratic boulders in Yosemite National Park. On the south side of Yosemite Valley the road cuts through a moraine. Alongside the road and at the edge of the moraine is a large erratic boulder. This boulder is composed of a granite that is found thirteen miles away on the Cathedral Range. It is

Erratic boulders in a moraine about a quarter of a mile east of Bridalveil Fall.

Erratic boulder near Sentinel Dome shows signs of weathering. Part of the rock has fallen off.

proof that the ice traveled from the Cathedral Range and down into the valley.

The erratic boulders in the uplands are evidence of how high the glaciers reached. There are several erratic boulders near the eastern base of Sentinel Dome. Long ago the ancient moraines disappeared, and the few erratic boulders that are left show signs of weathering.

In the formation of Yosemite Valley the river eroded part of the rock, and the glaciers removed the rest. The river had cut a deep V-shaped chasm over a period of twelve million years or more before the great ice age, and it continued to erode a V-shaped valley between glacial stages. Although the glaciers were in the chasm a comparatively short time, about a million years, they excavated the rocks quickly, because they had more digging power and a larger eroding surface than the river. The walls of a V-shaped valley will not allow a glacier to spread out; therefore the confined ice becomes thicker and fills the valley. Because the ice pushes against the lower sides of the valley, it can excavate a larger area than a river and make the valley wider at the bottom, creating a U-shaped valley.

Glaciers easily dug away canyon sides where the rocks had been cracked by many joints. A joint is a fracture along which no apparent dislocation or movement has occurred. Most of the joints were created when the hardened granite fractured under the release of stresses and strains.

The drawing at the left shows the V shape of a river-eroded valley while the drawing at the right shows the U shape of a glaciated valley. The dotted line indicates how high the top of the glacier reached.

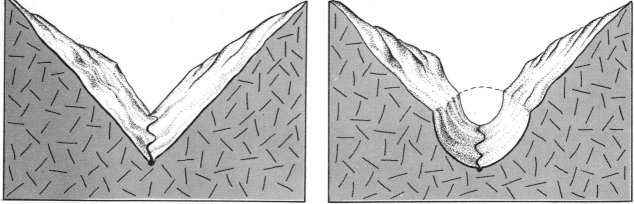

This drawing shows a cross section of the present glaciated Yosemite Valley. The dotted lines indicate the profiles of the three former valleys.

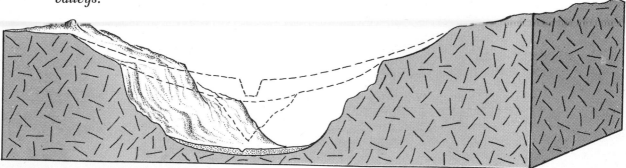

On top of this upland mound, which can be seen from Tioga Road, are multijointed rocks, while the lower part has less-jointed rocks. The latter are cracking and falling off in layers. Possibly at one time the whole hill was covered with multijointed rocks. If the glacial age had continued, the whole top of the mound would probably have been carried away.

Unjointed rocks were more difficult for a glacier to pluck out. It could not dislodge rocks that were fifty to hundreds of feet long and ten or more feet thick. They were too massive. Where the glacier could not remove the rocks, it ground, smoothed, and scoured them with sand and mud, making a surface over which it slid easily. In some places the rocks were highly polished, although much of the glossy surface has been chipped off since the glaciers melted.

Murphy Dome, which is on the Tioga Road, reveals some glacial polish and horizontal striations.

Glacial polish on Polly Dome, which is at the eastern end of Tenaya Lake on Tioga Road.

Boulders and rocks embedded in the ice pushed against and carved the polished granite beneath the glacier, making parallel scratches and grooves. As boulders and rocks ground over the bedrock, some finely powdered particles of rock were worn off their surfaces. This powdered rock is called glacial flour.

It may be difficult to realize how the glacier could create such a shiny surface, but a layer of ice 1000 feet thick puts a weight of about thirty tons on every square foot of bedrock. Glaciers, thousands of feet thick, wound their way down from the high mountains, filling river valleys and overriding the tops of many high mountains and domes. It is not too difficult to imagine these

Looking eastward from Glacier Point, this view of the lower end of Tenaya Canyon shows the glaciated U-shaped canyon. To the east of Half Dome the canyon wall is about two miles long. Its topmost peak is Clouds Rest, which is about 4700 feet above the canyon floor.

gigantic masses of ice, with their tremendous eroding power, quarrying over thousands of years the billions of tons of rocks which filled the now empty spaces.

Before the ice age and during the interglacial periods the river flowed at the bottom of the chasm and eroded the valley into a V shape. But the glaciers changed the shape of the valley. The great weight of the ice and its powerful excavating action sculptured the valley and its walls into a great U-shaped trough.

Although the glaciers carved Little Yosemite Valley into a U shape, they were unable to dig it very deep, because its granite was sparsely fractured and therefore resisted extensive erosion. The

The speed of Bridalveil Creek as it flows down its hanging valley causes the water to shoot outward before it drops, making a free leap over a 630-foot precipice. In the afternoon when the sun is shining on the spray one can see a rainbow. The daily up-valley winds and nightly down-valley winds puff out the spray in lacelike patterns.

glaciers could not remove either Mount Broderick or Liberty Cap, because the domes were too massive and solid. Nor were the glaciers able to remove the wall-like ridge that is west of the two domes and north of the upper Merced River. The top of the ridge is called Grizzly Peak.

Some of the valleys and canyons in Yosemite National Park have glacial stairways, a series of steplike terraces which are of various lengths and have irregular heights. A glacial stairway was created when a glacier excavated the well-jointed, easily quarried rocks above the treads but was unable to dig away the unfractured rocks that form the risers.

One such stairway can be seen below Little Yosemite Valley. The Merced River drops over the glacial steps to make Nevada and Vernal Falls. The steps have sharp edges and fairly level treads. The upper or Nevada Fall has a sheer front of 600 feet while the lower, Vernal Fall, drops 300 feet.

Most of the lakes in the Sierra Nevada are the result of glaciation. Where there was an area of much-fractured rocks, the glacier in its downward path gouged out a hollow. Usually at the lower edge of such a basin there was a section of unfractured rock, like the riser of a glacial stairway, which the glacier could not remove and which became a dam. As the glaciers melted, water filled the basins, creating lakes, many of which are now fed by small streams, melting snows, and springs.

This drawing shows how the much-jointed rocks were plucked out, leaving the less-jointed rocks. The upper broken line represents the valley floor before it was glaciated. The thin lines below it show the stages of glacial erosion, the result of plucking and abrasion.

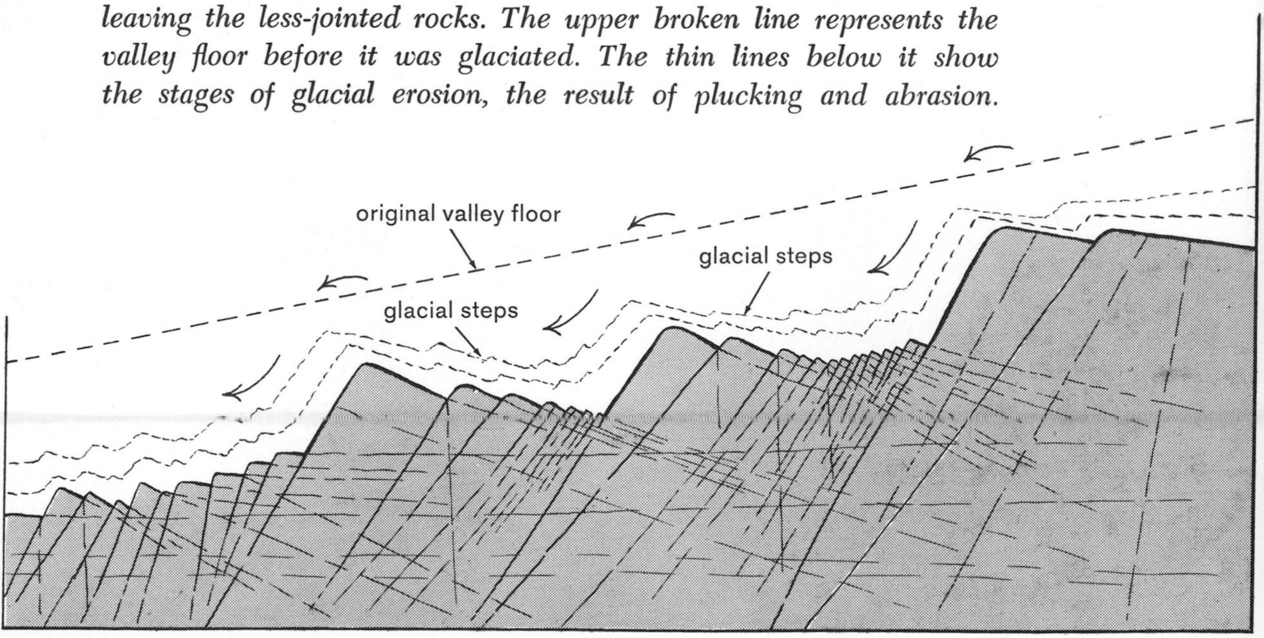

original valley floor

glacial steps

glacial steps

Looking eastward toward Little Yosemite Valley above Vernal and Nevada Falls are Liberty Cap and, to the north of it, Mount Broderick.

The view from Tioga Road from the west includes, on the left, Polly Dome and Tenaya Lake, and, the right, Tenaya Peak. As far as is known, the lake below the peak is unnamed.

At the end of the glacial period Yosemite Chasm became a lake. The moraine left by the last glacier formed a dam near Bridalveil Fall. When the glacier melted, its waters were imprisoned. Ancient Lake Yosemite was five and a half miles long and about as wide as the present valley. Geologists have taken seismic soundings which show that the ancient lake formed deposits which are now as much as 1200 to 1800 feet below the valley floor.

Gradually the lake filled with rock, gravel, and soil until it became shallow. Then grasses and trees encroached upon its edges until there was only a flat valley floor.

Mirror Lake at the lower end of Tenaya Canyon is an example of how ancient Lake Yosemite was filled with deposits. This lake, which is now a shallow pond, is slowly filling up. Grass is growing into the water, followed by deciduous trees at the edges, and the conifer forest is advancing.

Mirror Lake was formed after the last glacial period by the damming of Tenaya Creek. The dam was created by rocks falling from the cliff sides under Half Dome and from the opposite wall under North Dome. Probably earthquakes dislodged some rocks, but most of them fell because water seeping into cracks and expanding into ice pried them loose; or because the ice, which is a cementing agent, melted and released the rocks. This process is going on today. Occasionally on frosty mornings, just after the sun is up, or

A sketch of extinct Lake Yosemite indicates its probable boundaries.

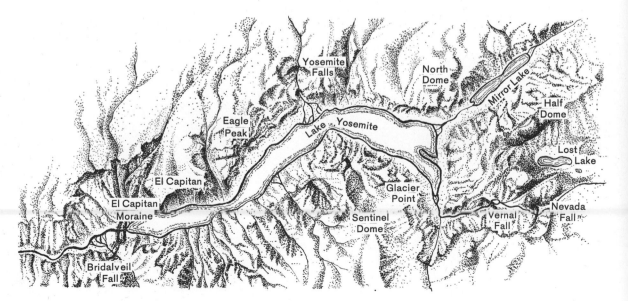

Looking eastward up Tenaya Canyon, Mirror Lake reflects Mount Watkins.

Tuolumne Meadows, seen from the western entrance, are the largest meadows in the Sierra. Once they contained a string of glacial ponds, which have now been filled with gravel, soil, and grasses. The conifers that are beginning to grow along its edge may someday become a forest.

in the late afternoon one can hear loud thunderlike claps and rumblings as rocks tumble down the valley's cliffs.

After the last glacial stage about 10,000 years ago, the climate changed, becoming even warmer than it is today. Then, sometime between 2000 and 4000 years ago, the climate turned cooler and snow started to fall again, forming glaciers. The twenty-odd glaciers presently active in the Sierra Nevada were formed in this recent period. Although these small glaciers remain stationary during the summer in shady basins at high altitudes, each year they are becoming smaller. One wonders if after the present ice age is completely over, another ice stage will begin. Eventually one may, but whether it will be soon, geologically speaking, or in hundreds of millions of years, we do not know.

CHAPTER 4

The Sierra Escarpment

During the great ice age the Sierra block started to rise, and the area to its east began to sink. The land slipped along the many lines of fractures that originally separated the Sierra block from the surrounding rocks. Many of these lines of fractures are faults. A fault is a fracture along which there has been displacement or movement. The fractures and faults vary from less than a mile to many miles in length and go down thousands of feet into the granite.

The earth's crust can move up, or down, or sideways along a fault. When the earth moves vertically, the exposed clifflike side is called a fault scarp. For hundreds of thousands of years a series of down-faulting movements gradually dropped the land to the east of the Sierra Nevada, creating an escarpment. An escarpment is a long line of high cliffs.

A profile drawing of the Sierra Nevada after the downfaulting of the eastern slope in the Mono Lake district.

old sedimentary rock

White Mountains

Mono Lake

Types of movement along faults.

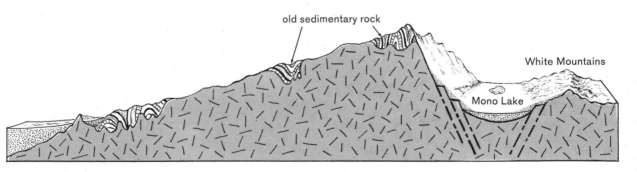

Vertical   Horizontal   Oblique

The Sierra escarpment seen from Owens Valley north of Bishop.

The escarpment above Mono Lake, seen from the east on Highway 120.

The Sierra Nevada escarpment is one of the most spectacular of its kind in the world. Along its 430-mile length its height above the valleys varies from 2000 feet in the north to 900 feet near its southern tip.

The most dramatic view of the escarpment is from Owens Valley, where the lack of foothills and the flat valley floor accentuate the height of the mountains.

Although the altitude of the Sierra crest is approximately the same above Mono Lake as in Owens Valley, the escarpment is not as spectacular.

CHAPTER 5

Granite Types and Master Joints

The walls of Yosemite Valley exhibit many rock forms which range from sheer cliffs through rounded and angular spurs to pinnacles and slender spires. The shape of the rocks was determined by two factors. One factor was the type of granite, the other was the way in which the rocks were fractured.

Granite is composed of both quartz and feldspar, which can be white, pinkish, or light gray. Besides these two minerals, most granites also contain some hornblende and mica, which usually are very dark gray. The types of granite and their colors depend chiefly upon the relative amounts of these four minerals. A large percentage of hornblende and dark-colored mica gives the rock a dark gray or even black color. A large percentage of quartz and feldspar makes up a granite that is very light gray.

Thirteen or more types of granite compose the rocks within Yosemite National Park. Each has a typical color, texture, and mineral content. Although these thirteen types of granite possibly originated from the same vast subterranean reservoir of magma, they did not all rise at the same time, but were pushed up in hundreds of upwellings over a period of twenty million years. In Yosemite National Park and throughout the Sierra, the light-colored granites are capable of withstanding the stresses and strains of internal pressures and did not fracture easily. The darker granites are fairly brittle and developed many fractures. They tend to decompose because their minerals are more susceptible to weathering.

When you look at the tiny crystals in a specimen and then at the massive rocks and cliffs formed from them, you cannot help but be impressed by the largeness and at the same time the minuteness of nature. It is almost impossible to think of how many billions of crystals there are in the rocks of Yosemite Valley alone.

The rocks around Cathedral Spires and the valley wall to the east are of a dark gray color. They are brittle, cracking in all directions, and therefore very susceptible to erosion. Since the glacial age, erosion by water, ice, and gravity has been rapid—as the talus

The southern wall of Yosemite Valley east of Cathedral Rocks.

slopes under the recesses and craggy spurs show. A talus slope
is an accumulation of fallen rocks at the base of a cliff.

The Rockslides, which are on the north wall at the western end
of Yosemite Valley, also have dark gray-colored rocks. The cliff
has broken into innumerable small rocks which have formed a talus

Talus slopes of the Rockslides, with Ribbon Fall at the right.

slope. The talus slopes in Yosemite Valley east of Bridalveil Fall are neither so wide nor so high as the slope of the Rockslides, because their debris has accumulated only since the last glacier passed. The last glacier terminated before it reached the Rockslides and did not carry its huge talus away.

Agassiz Column on Washington Point shows different kinds of joints.

Not only did the rocks of the walls break into smaller pieces but they also split along extra-large cracks, called master joints. These occurred along lines of structural weakness within the rocks. The shape of the large rocks and cliffs was determined by the direction of the structural weakness within them. There are three directions in which the joints cracked—vertical, or straight up and down; oblique, or slanting across from top to bottom; and horizontal, or across from side to side.

An example of vertical fracturing is found in the clifflike walls around the waterfalls. Most of the cliffs have vertical planes of weakness behind and parallel to their faces. It was along these planes of weakness that the rocks cracked. These rocks are composed of a granite which has a tendency to separate into sheets and erode by splitting off one sheet at a time. The sheets might be

Yosemite Falls, looking northeast.

imagined as slices of bread in a gigantic sandwich loaf of irregular width.

A good example of a sheet can be seen at Upper Yosemite Fall, which is located on the northern side and about in the middle of Yosemite Valley. If one faces the fall, the cliff to the right can be seen to be fractured in nearly vertical sheets, slanting at an eighty-degree angle. There is a remnant of a sheet in the form of a 1500-feet-high, thin, narrow pinnacle still clinging to the wall. This remnant is called the Lost Arrow.

On both sides of Lower Yosemite Fall there are two master horizontal joints. Bushes can be seen growing along them. Above the joints to the west of Upper Yosemite Fall is an incline that was formed by a master oblique joint. It is possible that at one time Yosemite Creek cascaded down this incline and at a later

Sentinel Rock, looking southward.

date some kind of obstruction about a mile up the creek changed its course.

Opposite Yosemite Falls, Sentinel Rock rises from a spurlike base. Its top reaches 3000 feet above the valley floor, which itself is 4000 feet above sea level. Sentinel Rock's sheer, smooth clifflike front and the splintered crest have a sheeted structure. Almost all the joints are vertical with the exception of a few that are oblique.

Half Dome is the most spectacular example of a vertical master joint in the valley. Its sheer wall-like face was formed along a great master joint. There never was another half to Half Dome. Instead, the "other half" was composed of rocks that fractured into parallel, vertical sheets much like Sentinel Rock. The sheets were eroded into a pile of rubble which the glaciers removed. Stubs and spurs remain at the base of the face, giving geologists a clue to its past structure. If there had been another half, it would still be standing, for neither the glaciers nor erosion could have destroyed it.

Reflected in the Merced River is Half Dome's 2200-foot-high wall-like face.

Glacier Point, at the east end of the southern wall, is made up of two types of granite. One is older than the other. The lower, eastern part of the point, which has been smoothed and rounded by glaciers, is the younger. This granite welled up underneath the older granite, which, like Sentinel Rock, has a sheeted structure. Every night during the tourist season the glowing embers of a fire are pushed over the top of the cliff by a crew of men. They make a firefall because the cliff is absolutely vertical.

Looking southeast to the left and at the bottom part of Glacier Point, one can see the smooth older rock. Its shininess is caused by water seeping from the melting snows. The cliffs to the right are formed of younger rock.

The photograph insert shows the firefall. The embers fall straight down 1000 feet. Glacier Point, which has an altitude of 7000 feet above sea level, is itself a little over 3000 feet above the valley floor.

The highest top of the group of the Three Brothers is Eagle Peak, seen here from the west. The Indians called the rocks "Leaping Frog."

The group of the Three Brothers, which is on the northern wall and east of El Capitan is shaped unsymmetrically. The eastern side is a vertical cliff. The western side is cut by three oblique master joints and three vertical master joints. Above the three oblique master joints the glacier took away small loose rocks, leaving

Looking eastward beyond the western side of El Capitan, one can see the salient or buttress that extends from El Capitan's southern wall.

three planes. The oblique planes dip at the same angle and rise progressively one higher than the other, like slanting roof tops. The glacier also removed rocks from the sides of the three vertical master joints, leaving three short cliffs. They give the appearance of walls supporting the roofs.

The western side of El Capitan shows that the upper half of the rock has been fractured along vertical lines while the lower half has a few oblique fractures.

El Capitan is the largest single exposed rock in the Sierra Nevada. Its long wall measures 4400 feet. Where the granite has been weathered it takes on yellowish or reddish tints. The color comes from iron which has oxidized. The cloudlike darker spots in the rock are intrusions of fine-grained granite called diorite.

From the southern side of the Merced River, when one looks northward, the entire length of El Capitan can be seen. The dark lines are streaks of lichen.

Looking southwestward, Cathedral Rocks are an example of vertical plane structure and of the durability of the light-colored granites.

CHAPTER 6

Domes and Exfoliation

In contrast to the angular cliffs and rocks are the rounded domes. Yosemite National Park has more domes than any other area of its size. in the Sierra Nevada or possibly anywhere else in the world. In fact, domes are very rare on this earth.

All domes are made up of unjointed rock and shed thin, curving shells of rock. One might think of a dome as being like an onion having thin skins which become progressively thicker toward the center until there is a hard core. Outer shells are thinner than those near the center. Shells measure from a few inches to ten or more feet thick.

Polly Dome on Lake Tenaya.

Exfoliating granite along Tioga Road.

The process of shedding shells is called exfoliation. Geologists do not know exactly why the domes exfoliate, but believe that one of the causes is load relief. Granite crystallizes at great depth and under great pressure. When the pressure upon it is relieved by the removal of the overlying rock, the surface of the granite slowly expands until lines of fracture develop. These fractures form shells that later fall away. The shell does not suddenly crack and fall off in one piece but gradually breaks into smaller pieces.

Domes were not always round but may have had angular edges and points that have become rounded as layers of curving shells were shed. As each shell fell off, a more domelike surface emerged. All unjointed masses of rock in the Sierra Nevada are prone to exfoliate. None of the domes is completely spherical but all are slightly egg-shaped. Nor do the masses of granite always take the shape of domes. Some are cylinderlike, forming spurs, buttresses, or ridges, such as the ridge behind El Capitan. Exfoliating shells can also be concave. In some places the glaciers excavated sparsely fractured rock into concave surfaces. These surfaces now exfoliate concave shells. Examples of concave exfoliation can be seen in the upper part of Tenaya Canyon.

The Royal Arches, which are on the northern wall of Yosemite Valley at the entrance of Tenaya Canyon, are the result of fracturing along crescent-shaped joints. The glaciers plucked away the loose and lower part of the arches so that the remaining shells are recessed one behind the other. The shells range from ten to eighty feet in thickness. The top shell, which is the thickest of all, is composed of several layers of thinner shells.

Royal Arches, North Dome, and Washington Column, looking northward. The largest arch is 1000 feet high and 1800 feet across.

Mount Starr King and a group of domes, looking eastward from Glacier Point. These domes along with Half Dome and Clouds Rest are the oldest in Yosemite National Park.

Sentinel Dome and Mount Starr King, located southeast of Glacier Point, have the most nearly perfect dome shapes. They were exfoliating shells at least twelve million years ago. Before the ice age, two other domes, Mount Broderick and Liberty Cap, were rounded knobs partially covered by rocks and soil. The backs of these domes have been smoothed by grinding, and their fronts were subjected to glacial plucking.

In the uplands there are many rounded, slightly exposed and bare granite swells which someday may become fully rounded domes. Underneath the uplands and behind Yosemite Valley walls there are probably many more incipient domes which in a future geological era may replace those of the present. Slowly the forces of erosion are uncovering the domes.

CHAPTER 7

Erosion in the Sierra

Erosion is the process of transporting debris that has been loosened from the rock by weathering. Mechanical weathering is the breaking, cracking, and splitting of rocks into smaller pieces by force. Chemical weathering is the disintegration and decomposition of rock caused by chemical reactions.

This conifer tree on the southern side of Sentinel Dome, by gaining a root hold, illustrates both mechanical and chemical weathering.

Earthquake boulders in the Merced Gorge. It is believed that at some time these huge rocks were shaken loose by an earthquake.

The prying loose of rocks from other rocks by the action of water when it expands to become ice is called frost-wedging. Frost-wedging occurs not only in winter, but also when there is a heavy dew or a little accumulation of water in the cracks. When this moisture freezes, it expands and the bursting pressure pries the rock loose.

All over the Sierra Nevada in the frost zone, rocks and tiny rock scales are frost-wedged from the surface of exposed rock. This

Looking westward from Tioga Road, the top half of Tenaya Canyon's southern wall shows the fluted structure caused by snow avalanches and frost-wedging. During the winter the chutes are filled with snow.

slow but steady process of frost-wedging tiny scales and mineral grains probably is responsible for more erosion than frost-wedging of large rocks, frost-induced avalanches, or snow avalanches. An avalanche is a mass of snow, ice, soil, or rock which suddenly and swiftly falls down a mountain or precipice.

Snow avalanches are not infrequent in Yosemite Valley and, when seen, are quite spectacular if accompanied by a settling cloud of snow. Most snow avalanches also carry down rocks from the walls of the valley. On unjointed and glacial-smoothed rocks, snow avalanches slowly wear away the surface. An example of avalanche sculpturing can be seen on the wall below Clouds Rest, where there are vertical hollows between vertical ridges.

Grass growing out of a crack. Moss and lichen growing on granite.

Chemical weathering can occur when rain falls through the air and collects carbon dioxide to form a weak carbonic-acid solution. This solution seeps into tiny cracks, and over a long period of time the cracks are deepened and widened by the action of the acid on the rock.

The feldspars, which make up more than half the minerals in the granite, are very susceptible to attack by acid and, once attacked, turn to clay. When the feldspars decompose, like inferior mortar between two bricks, the other mineral crystals are loosened and separate from the granite rock. The quartz is not changed, and the grains form sand.

A stronger and quicker-acting solution is made when rain comes in contact with decaying plant matter. In small hollows on the rocks where a little dirt has accumulated, a small plant or grass seed can start growing. After the plant dies, its leaves, stems, and roots decay and form acid. The acid alters the rock to create a bit of dirt. In these openings the water and the dissolved minerals make up a certain amount of plant food. As the cracks enlarge, small bushes are able to grow. Roots of large bushes and trees pry the cracks farther apart until the rock splits. This prying loose of rock is an example of mechanical weathering.

Decomposed granite along the Glacier Point Road.

Some granite is so porous that the acid solution can soak down or percolate through it and in time decompose the whole rock. Most of the decomposed granite in the Sierra Nevada has been under a blanket of soil and vegetation which contributed to its decay. Examples of decomposed granite are found all over the Sierra. If you pick up a small piece it will crumble in your fingers.

Lichen on top of an erratic boulder near Sentinel Dome. The granite shows excessive weathering.

Many of the valley cliffs are covered with billions of lichens which grow down the sides of the rocks. A lichen is a combination of fungi and an algae that live together as one plant. On the south side of the valley, because it is protected from the sun, the lichens cover a large area of the rock surface. They give a uniform dark gray color to the walls, and one can tell by their absence where rocks or rock sheets recently have fallen. By contrast, the fresh, unweathered granite looks extremely bright.

On the north side, because the sun causes most of the moisture to evaporate, the lichens grow where seeping water has trickled down the walls. The lichen's very dark gray color, almost black, makes the cliffs look as though they had been streaked by dirt. The lichens secrete an acid which slowly reacts with the minerals in the

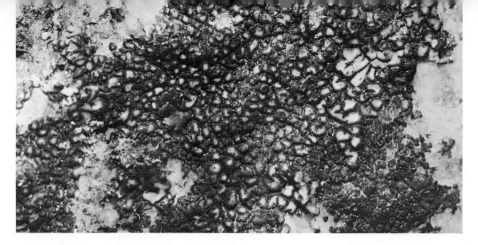

This photograph of lichens growing on granite is greatly enlarged. These lichens are found in extremely moist places while other varieties need less moisture.

rocks until they become loose and are removed. When a lichen dies, it drops off, carrying with it additional rock particles.

The soup-plate-size hollows, called solution pits, that are found on top of rocks in the uplands were probably produced by weathering, although geologists are not certain of the process involved.

Erosion is continual, whether it is by frost-wedging small rock scales, rain-borne acid loosening granite crystals, or lichen etching away the rock surface. Snow avalanches, rock avalanches, and earthquakes shake and dislodge rocks, enlarging talus slopes. Rain loosens the upland soil, carrying it down the valley's sides to deposit it onto the valley floor and eventually into the river.

Solution pits on top of a rock on Glacier Point.

Merced River in Yosemite Gorge, looking eastward. Depending upon the amount of melted snow and rain it contains, the river has a muted or deafening roar.

The river is still excavating the valley. During floods, boulders crash against each other with thunderlike claps and boomings and break up other rocks by knocking them together. The rushing water rolls pebbles about, while soil is carried in the muddy water down to the San Joaquin Valley.

Eastern end of Yosemite Valley.

We do not know what the valley will look like in the future. We can be certain that forces are constantly tearing down and building up, eroding the land in one place and creating mountains in another. Perhaps in some future geological era when the Sierra Nevada have been leveled, the sea will again invade the land. But Yosemite Valley will not change perceptibly in our lifetime and we can glory in its grandeur.

Appendix

Geologists have divided the intrusive bodies of granite within Yosemite National Park into age groups of series. Four of these
intrusive bodies are in the uplands and eastern part of the valley
and cover a hundred or more square miles. They are called the
Tuolumne Series and are the younger of the intrusive rocks. Most
of the five intrusive bodies in the western half of the valley are
smaller and have intruded upon each other in a complex pattern.
They are called the Western Series and are older than the Tuolumne
Series. There are four minor intrusive bodies that are scattered
over the middle and western sections of the valley.

The granites of Yosemite National Park are composed of the
following minerals. *Feldspar* contains either potash or lime plus
sods. Potash feldspar commonly has a slight pinkish cast. Soda-lime
feldspar is pearly gray. (Because the feldspar crystals reflect the
sunlight, the Sierra is often called the "range of light.") *Quartz*
is most often colorless, but it may be tinged grayish brown or
pinkish. In these granites quartz did not form crystals but hardened
into small shapeless masses. *Biotite mica* occurs as a black, hexagonal
crystal which flakes into thin plates. When mica crystals are washed
down into the river and are leached, their color changes from
black to yellow. Quite often these river-washed flakes are mistaken
for gold. Therefore they are nicknamed "fool's gold." *Hornblende*
is also black with sometimes a greenish tinge. Its crystals are
elongated.

Because Half Dome is composed entirely of one kind of rock,
its granite is called Half Dome Quartz Monzonite. Of the Tuolumne
Series, Half Dome Quartz Monzonite is the largest of all the granite
bodies in Yosemite National Park. It covers the area from the eastern
end of the valley far back into the Sierra Nevada. The quartz
monzonite forms massive rocks, such as the domes and mile-long
cliffs, and tends to be sparsely fractured.

Half Dome Quartz Monzonite is usually fairly uniform in its
medium-grained texture and medium gray color. The black mica
flakes are a quarter of an inch wide and the hornblende prisms are
about a quarter of an inch long. The soda-lime potash crystals
are more numerous than the larger potash feldspar crystals.

Half Dome Quartz Monzonite. Actual size.

Cathedral Peak Granite is another intrusive body of the Tuolumne Series. It covers part of the Cathedral Range and part of the Tuolumne Meadows. Cathedral Peak Granite is easy to recognize once you have seen it because of its large pinkish gray, opaque crystals of potash feldspar. These crystals are from half an inch to four inches or more long, and from a quarter of an inch to an inch or more wide. Weathered boulders are studded with these crystals, which protrude from a light gray and medium groundmass consisting of quartz, both feldspars, some mica, and a little hornblende.

Also of the Tuolumne Series is Sentinel Granite. It has a tendency to form sheeted structures such as Sentinel Rock, Upper Yosemite Fall, and the top of Glacier Point. It is usually medium dark in

Cathedral Peak Granite. Actual size.

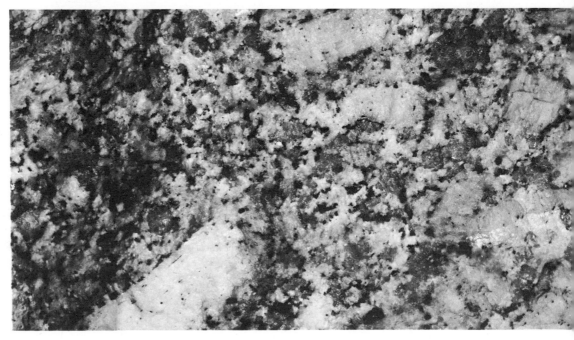

El Capitan Granite. Actual size.

color with a medium-grained texture. But it varies both in texture from coarse to fine and in color from dark to light.

The name El Capitan Granite is misleading because it implies that the rock El Capitan is composed wholly of this granite—which is untrue. The massive rock is an example of how several types of granite can intrude upon one another in a complex pattern. Of the Western Series, El Capitan Granite can be identified fairly easily because its crystals of potash feldspar are about half an inch long, flesh tinted, and somewhat transparent. On weathered surfaces the crystals protrude. The groundmass is of whitish soda-lime feldspar and brownish gray quartz. The granite contains a little mica but has very little if any hornblende.

El Capitan Granite tends to form massive, unfractured, smooth, sheer cliffs, of which El Capitan, Cathedral Rocks, the eastern faces of the Three Brothers, and the Merced Gorge are examples. It also composes Sentinel Dome, the only dome which is not of Half Dome Quartz Monzonite.

The Rockslides are made up of both Hornblende Diorite and Hornblende Gabbro. These rocks are of the Western Series. Usually diorite is dark greenish gray but it can be various shades lighter. Its texture varies from medium- to very coarse-grained. Usually gabbro is very dark gray, almost black, but it also can be various shades lighter. It is both medium- and coarse-grained. Because these diorite

This picture of massive Cathedral Rocks and the Cathedral Spires shows the difference between the types of granite. That of Cathedral Spires is dark, brittle, and broken into many fractures while in contrast the granite of Cathedral Rocks is light-colored and forms a solid vertical-plane structure.

and gabbro rocks can be colored either very dark or light, and their textures can be either medium or coarse, they are not always easily distinguished one from the other. Often the two types of rock look exactly alike, and only by knowing their mineral composition can one tell them apart. In fact, this is true of most rocks in the valley.

YOSEMITE NATIONAL PARK
CALIFORNIA

Crown Point

Benson Lake

Lake Eleanor

Hetch Hetchy Dome

North Peak

TUOLUMNE RIVER

HETCH HETCHY RESERVOIR

Grand Canyon Of The Tuolumne

TIOGA PASS ENTRANCE

Mt. Dana

Tuolumne Meadows

Cathedral Peak

Mono Pass

Polly Dome

Murphy Dome

BIG OAK FLAT ENTRANCE

Road

Tioga

Crane Flat

Tenaya Lake

KUNA CREST

CATHEDRAL RANGE

Blacktop Peak

Yosemite Creek

Clouds Rest

YOSEMITE VILLAGE

North Dome

Yosemite Falls

Mt. Maclure

Lyell Glacier

El Capitan

Half Dome

Mt. Lyell

Tunnel

Glacier Point

Merced

River

Vernal Fall

Nevada Fall

Bridalveil Fall

Tunnel

Mt. Clark

EL PORTAL

Illilouette Creek

Merced

River

ARCH ROCK ENTRANCE

Buena Vista Crest

SCALE OF MILES

1   5

Chiquito Pass

Wawona Point

Mariposa Grove

SOUTH ENTRANCE

Glossary

APLITE   a kind of durable granitic rock made up almost entirely of light-colored minerals with a uniform fine-grained texture.

AVALANCHE   a large mass of snow or ice, sometimes including soil, rocks, and plants, that moves quickly down a mountain slope.

BEDROCK   a solid rock of earth's crust. It can be either exposed at the surface or overlaid with other rocks or soil.

BLOCK MOUNTAIN   a mountain formed by the uplifting of a single block of rocks.

BUTTRESS   a supporting rock wall.

CIRQUE   a steep-walled, semicircular recess in a mountain side formed at the head of a glacier.

CRUST   the outermost rocky layer of the earth.

DIKE   a thin sheet of igneous rock that cuts across older rocks and was created by an intrusion of magma into a fracture.

DOME   a large, rounded rock surface.

EROSION   the action of loosening, dissolving, and removing rock material from any part of the earth's surface by one process or a group of processes. These processes include weathering, solution corrosion, and transportation.

ERRATIC BOULDER   a boulder transported by a glacier and commonly of a different kind of rock from the bedrock upon which it rests.

ESCARPMENT   a long line of cliffs.

EXFOLIATION   the shedding of shells from rock surfaces.

FAULT   a fracture along which there has been displacement.

FAULT BLOCK   a mass of bedrock bounded by faults.

FAULTING   the movement that produces displacement of adjacent rock masses along a fracture.

FOLD   a bend in a stratum.

FORMATION   any unit of the same kind of rock that is different from the surrounding rock and usually large enough to be shown on a geological map.

FRACTURE   a break in a rock.

FROST-WEDGING   the prying loose of rocks from other rocks by the action of water when it expands to become ice; a type of mechanical weathering.

GLACIAL STAGES   the times when parts of continents were covered with ice in the form of glaciers and ice fields.

GLACIAL DEBRIS   boulders, rocks, pebbles, sand, silt, and mud carried by glaciers and deposited when the ice melts.

GLACIAL FLOUR   powdered rock, a product of erosion by glaciers.

GLACIAL POLISH   a shining surface on rocks produced by the polishing action caused by the passage of a glacier.

GLACIAL STAIRWAY   the treadlike levels of a glaciated valley.

GLACIER   a river of ice moving slowly down a valley.

HANGING VALLEY   a tributary valley whose floor is higher than the floor of the main valley at the point where the two valleys join.

ICE FIELD   a thick sheet of ice spreading and covering a large area.

INTRUSIVE ROCK   a rock formed when molten rock material or magma was forced up into older rocks and solidified while still beneath the earth's surface.

IGNEOUS ROCK   a rock formed from magma solidified by cooling.

JOINT   a fracture in a rock along which no apparent dislocation has occurred.

LOAD RELIEF   the relief from the removal of weight or pressure upon a rock which results in the rock expanding.

MAGMA   molten rock material within the earth which forms igneous rock upon cooling.

METAMORPHIC ROCKS   rocks changed by pressure and heat.

MOUNTAIN SYSTEM   a group of several more or less parallel mountain ranges.

MORAINE   rocks and soil deposited by a glacier, commonly in the form of a ridge.

OXIDIZE   to unite with oxygen.

PLANE   a flat surface.

SCARP   a cliff.

SEDIMENTARY ROCK   rock formed when accumulations of sediments, organisms, or dissolved materials that have been transported by water, wind, or ice become compacted and cemented.

SHEETS   thin layers of rock.

SHELLS   a curved layer of rock, usually mechanically pried loose from its parent rock.

SPUR   a projection of a mountain side or range.

STRATUM   a single sedimentary layer of the same kind of rock. (Plural: strata.)

TALUS SLOPE   an accumulation of fallen rocks that has formed a slope at the foot of a cliff.

UPLIFT   raising of part of the earth's surface above the surrounding area.

WEATHERING   a chemical or mechanical process, such as action of plant acids, air, water, and changes of temperature, that cause the rock to decay and crumble.

Suggested Reading

DYSON, JAMES F., *The World of Ice.* New York, Alfred A. Knopf, Inc., 1962.

MATTHES, FRANÇOIS E., *François Matthes and the Marks of Time.* San Francisco, The Sierra Club, 1962.

MATTHES, FRANÇOIS E., *Geological History of Yosemite Valley.* Professional Paper 160, United States Geological Survey, Washington, D.C., 1930.

MATTHES, FRANÇOIS E., *The Incomparable Valley.* Berkeley, University of California Press, 1950.

MUIR, JOHN, *Studies in the Sierra,* ed. by William Colby. San Francisco, The Sierra Club, 1960.

MUIR, JOHN, *Yosemite.* Garden City, N.Y., Doubleday & Company, Inc., 1962.

MUIR, JOHN AND ANSEL ADAMS, *Yosemite and the Sierra Nevada.* Boston, Houghton Mifflin Company, 1948.

SWIFT, HILDEGARDE HOYT, *From the Eagle's Wing.* New York, William Morrow & Company, 1962.

Geological Timetable

ERA	PERIOD	YEARS AGO	EVENTS IN YOSEMITE NATIONAL PARK AREA
Cenozoic	Quaternary		New cirque glaciers appear during the last 3000 to 4000 years.
			Glaciers disappear.
			Valley glaciers form and carve U-shaped valleys.
		1.5 – 2 million	The great escarpment is formed as the mountains are uplifted. Faulting movements continue at intervals along the eastern edge of the Sierra block.
	Tertiary		At the end of the Tertiary period and continuing into the Quaternary period the last and greatest uplift of the Sierra block occurs. The mountains reach essentially their present height. The rivers begin to cut V-shaped valleys.
			For a long interval the Sierra block remains comparatively stable. During this time deep and broad valleys are cut on the western slope.
			The Sierra block is uplifted several thousand feet above the land to the east.
			Volcanic eruptions cover the northern half of the Sierra with lava. Small local flows occur in the southern half.
			A series of minor uplifts slowly raises the eastern side of the Sierra block to form a low mountain range which tilts toward the west.

ERA	PERIOD	YEARS AGO	EVENTS IN YOSEMITE NATIONAL PARK AREA
			Hills become low mountain ridges.
		65 million	The lowland, far inland from the Pacific Ocean, is gradually upwarped.
Mesozoic			Long and continued erosion wears mountains down, and the Sierra region is reduced to a lowland with northwest-trending hills.
			Enormous masses of magma well up underneath and invade the folded strata. The magma cools to become granite.
			The Mesozoic sediments and underlying remnants of Calaveras Formation are folded, crumpled, and raised into the second ancestral mountain system.
			Volcanic and marine sediments thousands of feet thick are deposited in the shallow seas over the sunken range. These become the Mariposa Formation.
		225 ± 5 million	The mountains are slowly eroded into low hills. The land sinks below sea level.
Paleozoic			Toward the end of the era, sediments are folded and uplifted to form the first ancestral mountain system.
		570 million	Thousands of feet of sediments accumulate in the sea to form the Calaveras Formation.
Pre-Cambrian			Not known.

Adams, Ansel, 18
Agassiz Column, 62
Aplite, 23, 91
Avalanches, 79, 91

Basket Dome, 15
Big Oak Flat Road, 23, 29
Bridalveil Creek and Valley, 11, 12, 13, 47
Bridalveil Fall, 10, 33, 47, 52, 61

Calaveras Formation, 21, 95
Cascade Fall, 31
Cathedral Peak Granite, 87
Cathedral Range, 40–41, 87
Cathedral Rocks, 60, 72, 88, 89
  height of, 11
Cathedral Spires, 59, 89
Cirques, 36, 37, 91, 94
Clouds Rest, 10, 33, 46, 76, 79
  height of, 46
Coast Range, 12

Dana Meadows, 36
Dikes, 23, 91
Diorite, 70, 88
Domes, 73–76, 91

Eagle Peak, 69
Earthquakes, 19, 52, 78
El Capitan, 10, 11, 33, 68, 71, 75, 88
  colors of, 70
  height of, 11
El Capitan Granite, 88
El Portal, 12, 33
Erosion, 22, 30, 42, 46, 48, 59, 77–85, 91, 95
Erratic boulders, 40–41, 82, 91
Escarpment, Sierra, 55–58, 94
Exfoliation, 74–75, 91

Faults, 55–56, 91
Feldspar, 59, 80, 86, 87, 88
Fool's gold, 86
Formations, 21, 91
Frost-wedging, 78–79, 91

Gabbro, 88–89
General Grant National Park, 15
Glacial flour, 45, 92
Glacial stairways, 48, 92
Glacier Point, 14, 15, 46, 66, 76, 83, 87
  described, 67
  firefall at, 66, 67
Glacier Point Road, 12, 15, 81

Glaciers, 16–17, 33–54, 92, 94
  extent in Park of, 34
Granite:
  aplite, 23
  domes of, 73–76, 91
  erosion and weathering of, 22, 30, 59, 77–85, 95
  exfoliation of, 74–75, 91
  formation of, 22–23, 95
  master joints of, 62–64, 68–70
  Sierra block, 23–28, 94
  types of, 59, 66, 86–89
Grizzly Peak, 48

Half Dome, 10, 33, 46, 52, 64, 65, 76, 86–87
Half Dome Quartz Monzonite, 86–87
Hanging valleys, 10, 31, 47, 92
Hornblende, 59, 86, 87, 88

Joints, 42, 43, 48, 62, 92
  master, 62–64, 68–70

Kuna Creek, 36

Liberty Cap, 48, 49, 76
Lichens, 71, 80, 82–83
Little Yosemite Valley, 46, 48, 49
Lost Arrow, 63

Magma, 22–23, 59
Mariposa Big Tree Grove, 13, 15, 16
Master joints, 62–64, 68–70
Matthes, François E., 17–18
Merced Gorge, 29, 78, 88
Merced River and Canyon, 9, 12, 21, 65, 71, 84
  ancient, 26, 28, 30–32, 42
  falls of, 48
Mica, 59, 86, 87, 88
Mirror Lake, 52, 53
Mono Lake, 11, 27, 55, 58
Moraines, 39–40, 52, 92
Mount Broderick, 38, 39, 76
Mount Starr King, 76
Mount Watkins, 53
Muir, John, 14, 16–18
Murphy Dome, 44

Nevada Fall, 48, 49
North Dome, 15, 52, 75

Old Inspiration Point, 10
Owens Valley, 57, 58

Polly Dome, 45, 51, 73

Quartz, 59, 80, 86, 87, 88

Ribbon Fall, 61
Rockslides, the, 60–61, 88
Royal Arches, 15, 75

San Joaquin Valley, 27, 84
Sentinel Dome, 41, 76, 77, 82, 88
Sentinel Granite, 87
Sentinel Rock, 10, 18, 64, 87
Sequoia National Park, 15
Sequoias, 16
Sheets of granite, 62–63, 92
Sierra Club, 16, 17
Sierra Nevada:
  described, 9
  escarpment of, 55–58, 94
  glaciers in, 33, 40, 48, 54, 94
  history of, 19–32, 94–95
  See also Granite
Solution pits, 83
Strata, 20–21, 92

Talus slopes, 60–61, 92
Tenaya Canyon, 46, 52, 53, 75, 79
Tenaya Lake, 45, 51, 73
Tenaya Peak, 51
Three Brothers, 68–69, 88
Tioga Road, 43, 44, 45, 51, 74, 79
Tuolumne Meadows, 36, 54

Vernal Fall, 48, 49

Washington Column, 15, 75
Washington Point, 62
Wawona Tunnel, 10
Weathering, 77–83, 92

Yosemite Falls, 14, 63, 87
Yosemite Lake (extinct), 52
Yosemite National Park, 20, 34
  founding of, 15
Yosemite Valley:
  discovery of, 9–11
  glaciers and, 16–17, 33–54
  named, 11
  origin of, 19–32
  preservation of, 13–16
Yosemite Valley Railroad, 12–13

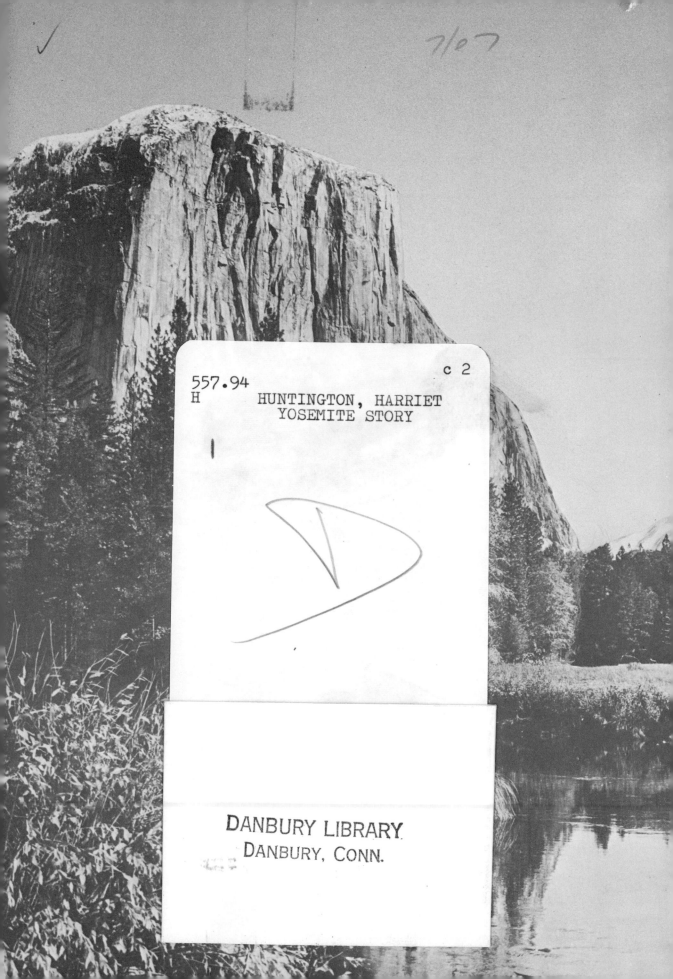